Garfield

The All-Round Sports Star

BY: JIM DAVIS

This edition first published by
Ravette Limited 1986
Reprinted 1987

Printed and bound in Great Britain
for Ravette Limited,
3 Glenside Estate, Star Road, Partridge Green,
Horsham, Sussex RH13 8RA
by William Clowes Limited, Beccles and London.

ISBN 0 948456 13 2

The All-Round Sports Star

In the next 80 pages you will see a healthy Garfield; running, jumping, throwing, catching, jogging and exercising!

Running wild with his imagination, jumping to conclusions, throwing down his food, catching 'forty winks',

jogging his memory and exercising his wit.
This according to Garfield, is essential for a healthy appetite!

PTOOEY!

OKAY, GARFIELD. NOW GIVE ME SOME HIGH LOBS

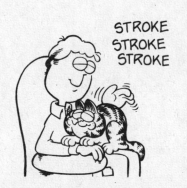

HAVE YOU EVER NOTICED HOW MUCH SOME PEOPLE LOOK LIKE THEIR PETS, GARFIELD?

HEE HEE

HEE

HA-HA HA

HA

12-2

JIM DAVIS

WOULD YOU LIKE TO COME IN, GARFIELD?

JIM DAVIS

12-9

© 1979 United Feature Syndicate, Inc.

12-16

© 1980 United Feature Syndicate, Inc.

1-20

JIM DAVIS

© 1980 United Feature Syndicate, Inc.

© 1980 United Feature Syndicate, Inc.

2-8

PUSH!

THIS TABLE WASN'T BIG ENOUGH FOR THE BOTH OF US

JIM DAVIS

POOMP!

JIM DAVIS 2-9

OOPS. I CRUNCHED JON'S ANTENNA

A LITTLE MORE TO THE RIGHT, GARFIELD

2-17   JIM DAVIS

IT'S NOT THE HAVING,
IT'S THE GETTING

2-24

JIM DAVIS

TIME TO PUT YOU OUT, GARFIELD

I DON'T WANNA GO OUT!

SLAM!

6-1

JIM DAVIS

HMMM, JON'S GOLF CAP

NO ONE DRIVES FASTER THAN THE GREAT ENZIO BODONI

ALMS FOR A TAP DANCING CAT

TAPPITY TAPPITY

CHECK THAT OIL, MISTER?

QUACK QUACK QUACK

10-5

SOMETIMES I WORRY ABOUT YOU, GARFIELD

HA HA HA HA

JIM DAVIS

CATS CAN BE BROKEN TO THE LEASH IF YOU JUST HANG IN THERE

JIM DAVIS

12-21

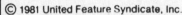

HEY, GARFIELD, WHAT SAY WE HAVE POTATOES FOR DINNER?

JIM DAVIS 2-25

GEE, IT'S BEEN A LONG TIME SINCE I FIXED POTATOES

© 1985 United Feature Syndicate, Inc.

TELL ME ABOUT IT

TRIVIA TIME, GARFIELD!

JIM DAVIS 2-26

WHAT'S THE ONLY SUBSTANCE ON EARTH HARDER THAN A DIAMOND?

YOUR LEFTOVER PIZZA

© 1985 United Feature Syndicate, Inc.

© 1985 United Feature Syndicate, Inc.

© 1985 United Feature Syndicate, Inc.

Other cartoon books published by Ravette

Garfield Landscapes

Garfield The Irresistible	£2.50
Garfield On Vacation	£2.50
Garfield Weighs In	£2.50
Garfield I Hate Monday	£2.50
Garfield Special Delivery	£2.50
Garfield The Incurable Romantic	£2.50
Garfield Another Serve	£2.50
Garfield Wraps It Up	£2.50

Garfield Pocket-books

No. 1 Garfield The Great Lover	£1.50
No. 2 Garfield Why Do You Hate Mondays?	£1.50
No. 3 Garfield Does Pooky Need You?	£1.50
No. 4 Garfield Admit It, Odie's OK!	£1.50
No. 5 Garfield Two's Company	£1.50
No. 6 Garfield What's Cooking?	£1.50
No. 7 Garfield Who's Talking?	£1.50
No. 8 Garfield Strikes Again	£1.50
No. 9 Garfield Here's Looking At You	£1.50
No. 10 Garfield We Love You Too	£1.50
No. 11 Garfield Here We Go Again	£1.50
No. 12 Garfield Life and Lasagne	£1.50

Introducing Snake	£2.50
Marmaduke Super dog	£2.50
Marmaduke 2	£2.50
Frank and Ernest	£1.95

All these books are available at your local bookshop or newsagent, or can be ordered direct from the publisher. Just tick the titles you require and fill in the form below. Prices and availability subject to change without notice.

Ravette Limited, 3 Glenside Estate, Star Road, Partridge Green, Horsham, West Sussex RH13 8RA

Please send a cheque or postal order, and allow the following for postage and packing. UK: Pocket-books – 45p for one book plus 20p for the second book and 15p for each additional book. Landscape Series – 45p for one book plus 30p for each additional book.

Name ....

Address ....

....